SECTION N UNDERPASS

SECTION N UNDERPASS

DAVID HENNINGHAM

Matador
9 Priory Business Park,
Wistow Road, Kibworth Beauchamp,
Leicestershire. LE8 0RX
Tel: 0116 279 2299
Email: books@troubador.co.uk
Web: www.troubador.co.uk/matador
Twitter: @matadorbooks

ISBN 978 1789016 413

British Library Cataloguing in Publication Data.
A catalogue record for this book is available from the British Library.

Printed and bound by CPI Group (UK) Ltd, Croydon, CR0 4YY
Typeset in 11pt Aldine by Troubador Publishing Ltd, Leicester, UK

Matador is an imprint of Troubador Publishing Ltd

CONTENTS

ACKNOWLEDGEMENTS

Thanks to the following companies who've allowed me to indulge in the delights of their nostalgic images:

Bauer Media
BP Archives
BT
Commodore
Ford of Britain
Hasbro
Heinz
Lucozade Ribena Suntory
Mastercard UK
Mondelez
Premier Foods
Unilever
Weetabix

ENTER THE SECTION N UNDERPASS

Carlton Krane admires the luscious green fields outside as the train speeds towards its destination. It's a familiar route and there are a number of markers that pinpoint the location. Slowing down, combined with a sharp left turn whilst the wheels on the track let off an unbearable screech, means we are on the outskirts of the big city. Once out of the left turn, it's 10 minutes of fast, fairly straight track. The fading advertising on the side of the disused trailer sitting in a field that reads 'Tent & inflatable bed rental www.tentsandbeds.co.uk' means we are entering the county where loads of music festivals take place in the spring and summer months - everyone calls the area 'Festival County'. There's then 10 minutes where the train crawls along due to the speed restriction. After the crawl, it's full throttle through the green fields for another 20 minutes, only slowing down when preparing to enter into our final destination station. Today's journey is uneventful - sitting in seat 22 in carriage B, whilst reading the newspaper. He's intrigued as the train slows down halfway through the full throttle green fields. Staring quizzingly out the window, Carlton notices the sign at the side of the track, 'Section

N railtrack' - it's an unexpected route onto an unknown stretch of track. Glorious sunshine is replaced with darkness as the train creeps into the tunnel ahead and comes to a halt. At a standstill engulfed in darkness, the engine abruptly shuts down and the carriage lights go out. Mobile phone screens illuminate the carriage as panic stricken discussions fly back and forth between passengers. The message from the onboard speakers is concise - 'We have arrived at our final destination - the train terminates here. Shortly the doors will open and you'll be helped safely off the train by our assistants based within the underpass. They will guide you to the nearest exits. Please ensure you have all your belongings with you. Thank you for travelling with British Rail - we'd like to wish you a pleasant life within the province. Goodbye.'

The usual journey has turned into a mind-boggling mystery. Carlton and his fellow passengers have arrived at the province within the Section N Underpass - a place where digital downloads, sleek flat screen TVs and contactless payments are replaced with cassette tapes, bulky convex screen televisions and wads of hard cash!

The Section N Underpass is a secret province devised by a few ordinary people - people who have become fed-up with the pressures of modern living. They've managed to recreate a province of simplicity with limited technological advancements - a place that fits their concept of living in the yester-years. Entering the province is not down to choice - it's down to chance! Some residents love living in the province whilst others hate it. For many, life in the province is all they know.

Finding himself in the utility room at the rear of his new home, Carlton comes across a shoebox containing typed letters, interviews, recollections, sketches and adverts.

For Carlton Krane, life in the province of the Section N Underpass has just begun.

LIST OF CHARACTERS

Sandra - general nosey parker and curtain twitcher
Dolly Enright - popular dessert maker and author of 'Royal Family Cooking'
Mary Undertrott - loyal wife
Davis J Daniels - local general practitioner
The Yeogrundy family - lovers of ice cream and lollies
Simon Matthews - retired office manager
Max Swain - Deputy manager at the casino and Monopoly expert
Lester Drake - late night television talk show host
Wilma Silver - Music journalist who wrote the controversial article 'Sex behind the speakers'.
Simon Greyhastle - underperforming teenager
Sarah Gamst - student with big imagination
Harry Greyleader - intelligent pupil at the local comprehensive school
Miss J Hastings - retired school teacher and avid knitter of children's clothes
Ian Autumntree - massive fan of the TV programme Grange Hill
Danny Smalls - Director at Sole 'n' Boot Footwear and fan of British Leyland cars
Sel - expert motor mechanic
Jack Remolsen - retired taxi driver
John Stoneyleigh-Smith - the voice of Access
Scott Manning - hilarious Eastender
Mrs R Raven - housewife at her wit's end
Judy Jacobson - host of 'Shift that Grime' television programme
Jill and Simon Kenrardy - unmotivated homeowners
Michael Stringers - retired factory worker

GLOSSARY

Curly Wurly: a curly, wavy, ladder shaped chocolate bar made by Cadbury's

Kate Bush: British music artist

Noel Edmonds: Breakfast DJ and TV presenter

Multi-Coloured Swap Shop: Kids television programme broadcast from 1976 -1982.

Castrol: Motor oil manufacturers

Freeman Hardy Willis: Footwear retailer 1877 - 1995.

Chinwag: A chat

Mad Lizzie: Lizzie Webb - daily fitness presenter and instructor on TV-am

The Green Goddess: Diana Moran - daily fitness presenter and instructor on BBC1's Breakfast Time

Stretch Armstrong: action toy figure that can be stretched and twisted into different shapes and positions

Ticker: the heart

Cheshire cat smile: fictional grinning cat in Lewis Carroll's 'Alice's Adventures in Wonderland'

A bit steep: being unreasonable

Tight-arse: someone who spends (or tries to spend) as little money as possible

Terry's chocolate orange: circular, segmented chocolate cut into segments

Paul Weller: singer in the music group 'The Style Council'

Atari 2600: games console launched in 1977

Wally: an idiot!

Eastender: someone who lives in or is from the east of London

Duck: friendly term used to address someone (commonly used in Derbyshire and Staffordshire)

THE FREEMAN HARDY WILLIS SHOEBOX

The brightly coloured geometric wallpaper causes Carlton to squint as he slowly turns 360 degrees, clocking various items around the living room. The blue murano glass fish sharing the mantelpiece with a collection of plastic deer ornaments. The mustard-coloured sofa with Curly Wurly and diamond-shaped red patterns. A four-buttoned television set with the indoor aerial slanted at a 45-degree angle on top. The cassette player and a scattering of cassette tapes sitting on the smoked-glass coffee table in the centre of the room. The ceiling decorated with white, vein-patterned polystyrene tiles. Tentatively, he sits on the edge of the sofa, leans forward, loads a cassette tape into the cassette player and presses play – the action sequence producing a 'clunk, clunk, click' sound. The song that crackles out of the speaker, Wuthering Heights by Kate Bush, initially adds to the mysterious atmosphere but eventually the song has a calming effect as it progresses. After pressing the stop button on the cassette player, he strolls over to the television, plugs it into the mains socket and turns it on by twisting the knob in a clockwise direction. The only available channels to watch are BBC1 and ITV! After adjusting the indoor television aerial, he sits back down on the edge of the sofa and watches Noel Edmonds host the Multi-Coloured Swap Shop. Sadly the only colours he can see on the television are black and white.

The last time he drank was at 7.30am – a cup of coffee made using the Nespresso machine. It was only a few hours ago that he was reading The Times newspaper and sipping coffee whilst sitting on a kitchen stool. A combination of a stressful journey and inhaling the warm, dusty charcoal air inside the tunnel meant he was gasping for a drink. With a gentle push, the kitchen door swings open. Seeing that its safe to enter, he slowly walks in and does another 360 degree scan – a three-tier orange-coloured vegetable rack stocked with potatoes, onions and carrots – a yellow larder pantry unit with various compartments – a freestanding gas cooker with the toasting compartment at the top. He fills the kettle with water, finds a box of Swan Vestas matches in a drawer and lights the hob. The kitchen has a two more doors – one on the immediate left and the other straight ahead at the end – he takes the door on the left.

After stumbling over a can of Castrol motor oil whilst entering the garage, he walks over to the car. The keys to the Ford Cortina are in the ignition and he can't help but jump in and start the engine. The engine kicks in on the second time of asking – twisting the ignition key whilst pumping the accelerator pedal did the trick. After a few minutes of hesitation, he decides against taking it for a drive and switches off the engine. A faint swirling sound is evident once back in the kitchen. The sound becomes louder whilst walking towards the door at the end. He pushes the door open with a gentle kick revealing the utility room with a twin tub washing machine in operation. Carlton gets that heart-in-mouth moment as the kettle starts whistling and dashes back to the kitchen to rescue it – he then heads back to the utility room. His face is splattered with steam as he opens the washer compartment. Once the steam has cleared, he watches the clothes being dragged around like a roller coaster. On the floor in the corner lies a Freeman Hardy Willis shoebox. No shoes in the box but instead filled with documents. Whilst sitting on the floor with his back against the rumbling washing machine, he examines the contents of the box – letters, sightings, interviews written using a typewriter – a narrator giving a brief overview of the subject matter at the start of many of them. His thirst is put on hold as the intrigue of the documents gets the better of him. The first document entitled 'Mr Kipling – The Master Baker and the tale of Sandra the nosey parker!'

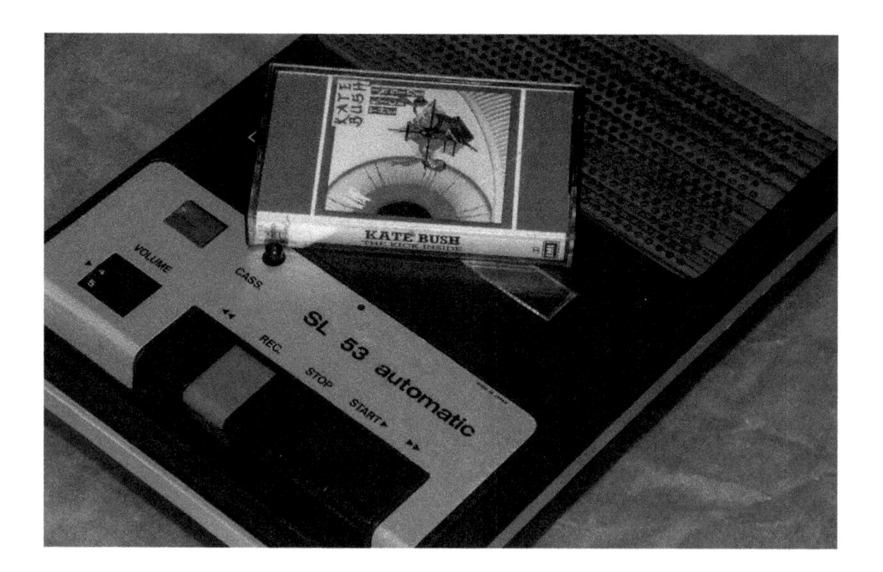

CLOSING COMMENTS:

CASSETTE TAPES

Dutch technology company, Phillips, perfected the design of cassette tape in the 1960s. Cassette tapes were a new form of portable entertainment launched at a time when vinyl and reel-to-reel ruled. At their peak in 1989, a massive 83 million cassette albums were sold in the UK!

It was common to see adverts for blank cassette tapes in magazines and on television – brands competing with each other whilst boasting about reliability and sound quality. Blank cassette tapes were essential for taping Top 40 chart songs from the radio.

Here are five popular brands of cassettes from yester-years along with their advertising straplines:

- Brand: TDK – 'Wait till you hear what you've been missing'
- Brand: BASF – 'BASF for the people who really know'
- Brand: Memorex – 'Memorex recording tape. Is it live, or is it Memorex?'
- Brand: Maxell – 'It's worth it'
- Brand: Scotch – 'Scotch recording tape. The truth comes out'

THE BLACK AND WHITE TELEVISION

Even though the first colour transmission took place on the BBC In 1967, 2017 figures show that 8000 homes in the UK are still using black and white television sets. The top ten areas still watching TV in glorious black and white are as follows:

1. London – 1596
2. Birmingham – 377
3. Manchester – 276
4. Glasgow – 176
5. Leeds – 138
6. Liverpool – 131
7. Nottingham – 105
8. Belfast – 90
9. Sheffield – 80
10. Omagh – 80

Brands of television sets that were popular back in the day were Pye, Decca, ITT and Ferguson.

THE FORD CORTINA TIMELINE

Maybe you got a buzz watching DCI Gene Hunt (in the BBC series Life on Mars) tearing around the streets of Manchester in his Cortina. Check out the selection of Cortina's below, choose one and let your imagination run free.

1962 - 1966: The original Cortina - mark 1.

1966 - 1970: Cortina mark 2

1970 - 1976: mark 3

1970 - 1976: mark 3

1976 - 1982: mark 4 and 5

1976 - 1982: mark 4 and 5

MR KIPLING

THE MASTER BAKER AND THE TALE OF SANDRA THE NOSEY PARKER!

The sweet aroma of baking engulfs a picturesque village in the province of the Section N Underpass. The aroma flows from a farmhouse kitchen on the outskirts of the village. Every morning at five, a van collects items of confectionery and delivers them to the village shops. There's rumours about the identity of persons working inside the farmhouse kitchen but nothing concrete. Below is a brief account from local resident, Sandra. She is the well known

nosey parker of the village and is always competing with her friends to dig-up gossip. Her account may shed some light on the identity of the baker.

> The sweet baking aroma always engulfs our village. I knew the aroma came from the farmhouse on the outskirts but wondered who was responsible. How many people were in the kitchen? A bit of investigation was needed …
>
> I ignored the small rusty 'beware of the dog' sign on the front gate – I'd kept an eye on the house using the binoculars I got as a retirement present and I never ever spotted a dog nor heard a bark! My husband stayed in the getaway car parked ten yards from the front gate and kept a lookout whilst I tiptoed between the apple trees and around the pond to where the kitchen was located at the back of the house. I peeked through one of the slightly steamy windows and saw a man. I'd say he was in his sixties. He was hunched over the worktop expertly rolling out pastry and he wore an apron. It was a bit blurry and wanting to get a closer look, I moved in closer until my nose pressed against the window. My initial sighting was confirmed! Happy with my mornings work, I decided to call time on this part of the investigation. After tiptoeing out through the front gate, I excitedly climbed into the getaway car. On the way back home, we discussed the complexities of the next part of the investigation … getting inside the farmhouse kitchen!

Later that evening, our neighbour who lives in the thatched roof cottage, Mrs Bailey, came round for a cup of tea and a chinwag. I casually let slip about my about my findings as she tucked into a slice of manor house cake. I watched her jaw drop with surprise and her face turn green with envy! I was chuckling to myself, knowing that I was streets-ahead of her for the latest task of 'Spotting the mysterious baker.' I was still chuckling after she'd abruptly left. I went into the kitchen and slid the remaining portion of manor house cake back into the box. The signature on the box read 'Mr Kipling'.

CLOSING COMMENTS:

- The Mr Kipling brand was launched in the 1960s by the company Rank Hovis McDougall.
- The actor, James Hayter, (1907 – 1983) was the original narrator for the Mr Kipling television adverts. The slogan, 'Mr Kipling makes exceedingly good cakes' is still fondly remembered and used.

MAKING AND CONSUMING ANGEL DELIGHT

BY MRS DOLLY ENRIGHT

A perfectionist in the kitchen, Dolly Enright takes pride in every dish she makes. When it comes to making Angel Delight, she makes sure the dessert is deliciously light every time. Angel Delight comes in a sachet – the sachet containing carefully blended ingredients to make a delicious dessert. Dolly believes there are ten steps to ensure the dessert is perfect and enjoyable every time.

Want something delicious and light? A dessert that won't make you feel like you've gobbled down a pile of bricks? Angel Delight is what you need!

How do you make the perfect Angel Delight? Here are ten easy steps to make the delightful dessert:

Birds
Angel Delight
3p OFF

1. Get a bowl and pour in some milk. Make sure you use cold milk straight out the fridge. Pull out a thermometer and make sure the milk is between four and eight degrees centigrade. You don't want your delightful dessert having cheesy off-flavours or odours, so use cold fresh milk!

2. Carefully open the sachet of Angel Delight, making sure you don't spill any. The powdered mix is like gold dust, so handle with care.

3. Carefully pour the powdered mix into the milk - pouring too fast may well produce puffs of Angel Delight smoke and inhaling it will make you sneeze uncontrollably. Snot and Angel Delight is a no no!

4. Beat it! Pull out that whisk and beat it. Show that mixture no mercy and beat it into submission until it's as light as an empty Cornflakes box.

5. After beating, place in the fridge and allow it to recover.

6. Serve. If you have the proper Angel Delight serving dish then spoon it into one of these. If not then use a bone china bowl. Don't spoil the dessert in the final stretch by serving in a coffee-stained mug.

7. Spoon dive. Clean spoon required (free from clumps of sugar or dried-on coffee stains). Enter at a 45-degree angle and glide into your mouth.

8. Enjoy. Feel the lightness of your creation on your tongue. Keep that spoon dive going at a constant, easy pace until the bowl is empty.

9. Never lick the bowl! It may be tempting, but remember, you're not a dog. Angel Delight is classy so show some respect. If you do end up licking the bowl, then Angel Delight is really not your thing - sell your house and go live in a kennel instead!

10. Self praise. If you've made it this far then give yourself a pat on the back - you've done it! Go on, boast about your achievement to your friends. Jolly well done to you!

CLOSING COMMENTS:

- Bird's launched Angel Delight in 1967.
- The first flavour launched was Strawberries and Cream.

CADBURY'S MILK TRAY

... ALL BECAUSE THE LADY LOVES MILK TRAY

Tom and Mary Undertrott have been happily married for 20 years. Their continual love for each other is evident when they look into each other's eyes and melt like ice cream in direct sunlight. However there is another man on the scene – a man that makes Mary weak at the knees… the Milk Tray Man. When the television advert for Cadbury's Milk Tray is shown, her eyes are glued to the handsome man dressed in black and she's overwhelmed with romantic thoughts. Reality kicks in when the advert is over and she looks at Tom's greying hair and football-round tummy. Mary gives a brief description of the Milk Tray advertisement below, along with a warning for men wanting to woo the ladies.

Choosing is half the fun

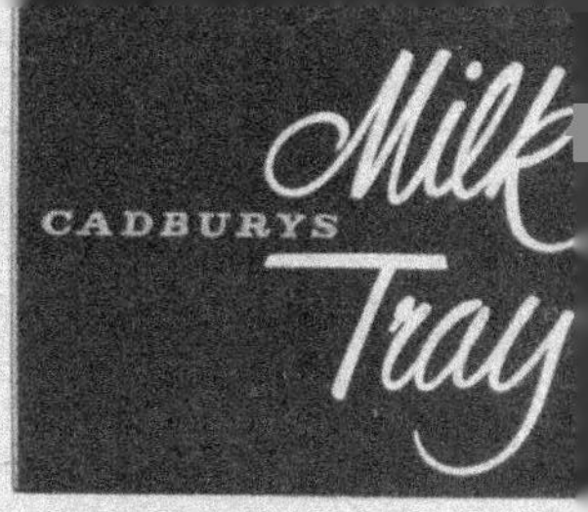

Milk Tray! Open the lid . . . fold back the lining paper . . . and now's the mom to choose. Turkish Delight? Almond Whirl? That mysterious one in gold pap They're *all* so delicious—that's your problem! And that, of course, is just v choosing is so much fun—when it's Cadbury's Milk Tray you're choosing!

He's cool, mysterious, athletic, tall, dark and handsome. Dressed in black with a briefcase attached to his waist, he displays his athleticism by confidently diving into the sea from a great height. Once in the sea, he skilfully evades the danger of a lurking shark. He's on a mission and there's no time for shark play until his mission is accomplished.

Arriving on the luxury boat a tad wet but still looking handsome, he enters her cabin, opens his briefcase and places a box of Milk Tray and his calling card by her bed - mission accomplished! Exiting the boat without a trace, he dives back into the sea with a diving knife clutched between his teeth for a bit of fun with his toothy friend.

A WORD OF WARNING (FOR MEN)

The Milk Tray Man is cool - he has an aura of irresistibility and indestructability. He also knows what a lady loves. Men are always looking for new ways to charm the ladies, but trust me on this one… do not dress up in all-black and sneak into her bedroom to leave a box of chocolates! Just because it works for the Milk Tray Man it doesn't mean it will work for you! Try explaining to the police how you were innocently climbing through her bedroom window late at night just to deliver a box of chocolates!

CLOSING COMMENTS:

- The Milk Tray brand was launched in 1915.
- The iconic Milk Tray Man first appeared in TV adverts in 1967.
- Gary Myers was the most recognisable Milk Tray Man – he played the role from 1968 – 1984.
- The iconic advert Mary refers to was filmed in the Blue Grotto on the island of Gozo.

LUCOZADE

IN SICKNESS AND HEALTH – ENTHUSIASTIC ADVICE FROM GENERAL PRACTITIONER DAVIS J DANIELS

Home remedies have become popular within the households of the province. The person responsible for the surge in popularity is local General Practitioner Davis J Daniels. He's well known in the region for encouraging residents to treat minor illnesses at home instead of piling into waiting rooms. As a result, bedside tables, bathroom cabinets and cupboards are stocked with various medicines and ointments.

Lucozade is popular drink that can be seen sitting on the bedside tables of the poorly, helping them regain health and vitality. Below, local GP Davis J Daniels talks about the benefits of Lucozade in both sickness and health. He also encourages residents to pursue a rigorous exercise regime at the end of their working day. 'Give stress a smack and keep the ticker healthy' is one of his famous sayings.

Lucozade
the sparkling GLUCOSE drink
replaces lost energy
"She has improved more than words can express"
Mrs. G.P.H., writes from Isleworth: ". . . I have been giving my little girl, aged 6, Lucozade for the past 4-6 weeks and she has improved more than words can express. Ever since she was born she has been difficult to feed . . . but recently she has eaten with relish . . ."
Give YOUR family Lucozade every day.
INVALUABLE IN SICKNESS AND IN HEALTH
Used by Doctors and Nurses in Hospitals, Clinics, Nursing Homes and Schools
LUCOZADE

In sickness

Feeling poorly? You may be out on your back like a sack of potatoes. Maybe that slight cough has turned into a spluttering monster making life miserable. Maybe you're in bed feeling low, lacking in energy without a glimmer of hope in sight? The journey towards recovery is aided by Lucozade!

The Lucozade bottle stands tall, concealed in a cellophane wrapper holding onto the power of recovery. It's the superhero in a bottle waiting to be gulped down by the poorly patient.

Once gulped down, things will start to turn around. Slowly but surely, you'll see a glimmer of hope at the end of the tunnel. You'll start feeling upbeat, energy levels will creep up and soon you'll be out of bed. The recovery sequence has three main steps:

Step 1: Relax and switch off. Slump into bed and wrap up well inside a duvet like an Egyptian mummy. Keep warm and get lots of rest!

Step 2: Eat well. It will be tempting to ditch a healthy meal and munch on sweets and chocolates instead - don't do it! Eat well - pack in the fruits, vegetables, soups and lean meat - they will help boost your immune system.

Step 3: Recovery. This is where Lucozade, the superhero in a bottle, steps in. Gulp it down and wait in anticipation as it begins to energise your body - Lucozade aids recovery!

In health - handy tips for exercising at home

Set your video recorder to record Mad Lizzie's session on TV-am (ITV) or the session with the Green Goddess on BBC1's Breakfast Time. Once home after a hard day's work, make space in the living room and drink a glass of Lucozade. Playback the pre-recorded exercise routine and join in by following the instructor's lead! If you want a more rigorous, burn-yourself-out workout then go for Lizzie's regime - on the other hand the Green Goddess' workout will loosen-up those tight muscles and you be as flexible as Stretch Armstrong!

Lucozade helps to pull you out the dark forest of sickness and gives you a boost during after work exercise. Lucozade - recovery during sickness and in health.

CLOSING COMMENTS:

- Glucozade drink was created by Newcastle based chemist William Hunter in 1927 to help his unwell daughter recover.
- The name Glucozade was changed to Lucozade just a few years later.
- In 1985 it was realised that Lucozade could be used as an everyday drink and the slogan was changed from 'Lucozade aids recovery' to 'Lucozade replaces lost energy'.

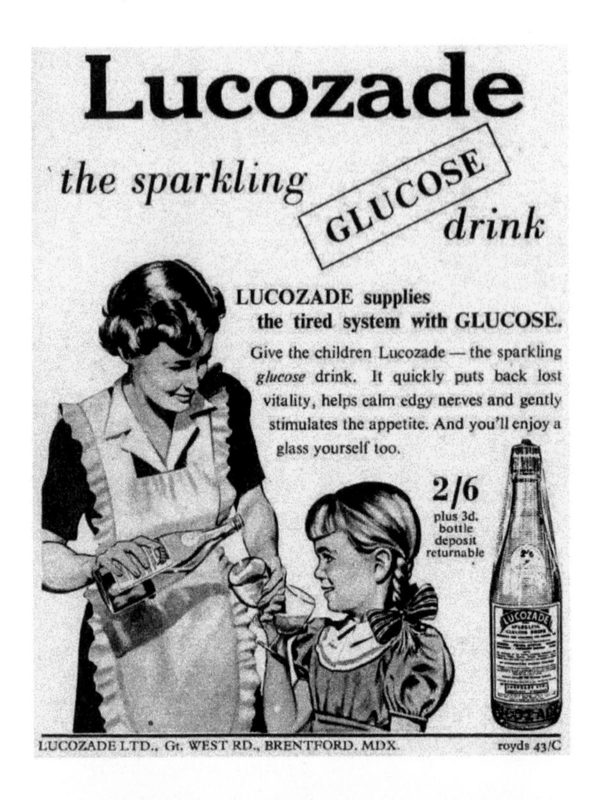
Lucozade
the sparkling
GLUCOSE
drink
LUCOZADE supplies
the tired system with GLUCOSE.
Give the children Lucozade — the sparkling glucose drink. It quickly puts back lost vitality, helps calm edgy nerves and gently stimulates the appetite. And you'll enjoy a glass yourself too.
2/6
plus 3d. bottle deposit returnable
LUCOZADE LTD., Gt. WEST RD., BRENTFORD, MDX.
royds 43/C

Lucozade
the sparkling
GLUCOSE
drink
replaces lost energy
for young and old
More and more parents every day are discovering that Lucozade is invaluable because it replaces lost energy so quickly and safely. Moreover, this delicious Glucose drink can be absorbed by the most delicate system without any difficulty whatever. Every member of the family needs Lucozade— especially in times of sickness. Get a bottle for your home.
2/6 plus 3d. bottle deposit (returnable)
8d. plus 2d. bottle deposit (returnable)
Lucozade is used by
DOCTORS and NURSES in CLINICS,
HOSPITALS, NURSING HOMES and SCHOOLS
Listen to
RADIO LUXEMBOURG (208 Metres)
MONDAYS 8-9 p.m.
and hear "SHOWTIME"
from THE LONDON PALLADIUM

WALL'S ICE CREAM

KEEPING COOL DURING THE SCORCHING SUMMER

Beautiful hot summer days are a regularity in the province of the Section N Underpass. The average temperature for the summer months is 31 degrees centigrade. Packed parks and green spaces are a common feature as people bask in glorious sunshine. The ice cream business peaks during these months – supermarkets, corner shops and ice cream vans are guaranteed booming sales. Ice cream, made by Wall's, is a must-have in freezers throughout the province. Mrs Justine Yeogrundy, mother of three, describes how Wall's ice cream keeps her family cool during the scorching summer months in the Section N province.

> The summer temperatures have become almost unbearable - the kids love it but my husband and I struggle with it. I'm always dashing around doing chores and the house becomes unbearably hot. My husband runs the local garage and complains that the some of the machines are too hot to handle during the summer months.

Soft Ice Cream for 1980

Things don't improve in the evenings - the air is more humid whilst the temperature stays static. After our evening meal, I'd get a Neapolitan block of ice cream out of the freezer, slice it into segments and serve in bowls. My husband, Jack, loves having some fruit cocktail with his ice cream. I'd watch the children separate the different segments of ice cream (strawberry, chocolate and vanilla) with their spoons, then gobble them down in random order. Afterwards we all felt a lot more comfortable and cooler - much needed relief inside our baking hot home!

The weekends are when we all go out together as a family. Greensilver Park is a popular destination for us - it has quite a big birdcage, an old fashioned water well with a bucket on a rope (luckily operated by a grown-up volunteer and not left to children!) and the usual play area with swings, slides and a roundabout. We take a packed lunch containing cheese sandwiches and a few packets of crisps. After we've eaten, the kids want their usual special treat of a Mini Milk ice lolly. They would run to the ice cream van by the entrance, get a place in the queue and wait for Jack and I to catch up. The ice cream man with the van, Luca, already knew our order - three Mini Milks and two Cornettos. We then find a nice spot under a tree and eat our ice creams in the shade.

CLOSING COMMENTS:

- The company, Wall's & Sons Ltd, began in a butcher's shop in St James' market, London (1786). In 1922, Wall's & Sons began making ice cream. The ice creams were initially sold from horse and cart on the streets of London. 'Stop me and buy one' tricycles eventually replaced the horse and cart – Wall's had 10 tricycles in 1922 but this increased to 8,500 in 1939!
- The 'Just one Cornetto' song was sung by Renato Pagliari for the advertising during the 1980s and 1990s – join in with the lyrics:
  Just one Cornetto,
  Give it to me,
  Delicious ice cream, of Italy
  Da da⋆ and chocolate dream,
  Give me Cornetto,
  From Wall's ice cream

⋆Indicates that the exact words are not clear – best to hum 'da da' at this point.

BEANZ MEANZ HEINZ

Ex-office manager Mr Simon Matthews and his wife are enjoying retirement in the province. Like some other residents of the province, the unexpected detour has turned out to be a blessing in disguise. He misses his two grandchildren who still live in the breakneck speed of modern society, but for him and his wife the province is happy, stress-free permanent retreat.

Below lies a poem he wrote whilst relaxing in the beautiful garden, reflecting on how Heinz Baked Beanz has been a reliable food source throughout his life.

A dip in the pool
Straight after school,
Need to be fed
Before my head hits the bed,
My first taste of Beanz Meanz Heinz.

University is not my adversary
Listen and learn
And eventually I'll earn,
Cash is scarce but it's survival of the fittest
Back to the halls
It's got to be Beanz Meanz Heinz.

The novice in the office
Finding my feet,
Typewriters tapping
Whilst others are flapping,
First day over
Thank goodness for that,
Relax and tuck into some Beanz Meanz Heinz.

The wedding day is long
But it goes in a flash,
A new life begins
But some things stay the same,
Beanz Meanz Heinz.

Our offer was accepted and contracts exchanged,
A sigh of relief as the day draws to a close.
Settle down and tuck into some Beanz Meanz Heinz.

I'm yawning at two in the morning,
Stumble to the cot and hum a tune.
Creep back to bed to rest my weary head,
Toast in the morning with Beanz Meanz Heinz.

Parents evening at school
We listen and nod,
'Needs to try harder', message from the teacher
No need to stress, there's many years ahead
Dinner at the table
Beans Meanz Heinz.

The nest is empty and time on our hands,
Overseas travel brings excitement and laughter,
Another holiday over and back to the nest,
Normality restored with Beanz Meanz Heinz.

The grandchildren keep us as fit as a fiddle,
Giggles and tears, day by day.
In the evenings, exhausted and peckish,
Beanz Meanz Heinz.

All of a sudden
A diversion occurred
An unexpected detour
To a province we now call home.

The afternoon snooze is a regular occurrence,
Hand in hand we stroll round the garden,
A short pause for breath as we admire the beauty,
Life is good but why so fast?
I turn to my darling and recall that day,
My first experience of Heinz Baked Beanz.

CLOSING COMMENTS:

- In 1869, American businessmen Henry J. Heinz and L. Clarence Nobel started Heinz and Noble. Their first product was grated horseradish in a clear glass bottle. Henry set up business with two of his relatives launching F&J Heinz Company.
- Production of Heinz products in the UK began in the 1920s. Prior to this, products were exported from America and Canada.
- During the World War Two, the Heinz factory in Harlesden (North West London) was vital in maintaining food resources – even though it was bombed at least twice, production still carried on.
- The Wigan factory (North West England) was opened in May 1959 – the factory produced beans.
- The slogan, A million housewives everyday pick up a tin of beans and say 'Beanz Meanz Heinz' began in 1967.

GRANDSTAND OR WORLD OF SPORT?

SPORT RULES ON SATURDAY AFTERNOON

SATURDAYS – ITV or the BBC? On Saturday afternoons, hundreds of people living in the province of the Section N underpass are glued to the television, inhaling hours of non-stop sport. Saturdays are when they switch off, get the essential chores done early, then spend the bulk of the day flicking between channels and choosing the sporting event that took their fancy. BBC have their sporting giant in Grandstand and ITV has World of Sport. It may be called 'tit for tat' between the two channels, each of them competing for attention on Saturdays. Two premium programmes, packed to the brim with various sports keeping the residents of the province rooted indoors.

THE STARTERS

Football is the taster as viewers mull over the choices of the main course. Delicious starters of Football Focus and Saint and Greavsie are served up on a small plate to get the sporting juices flowing. BBC's Football Focus, hosted by Bob Wilson, is the more serious offering whilst Ian and Jimmy hosted a more light-hearted offering on ITV.

THE MAIN COURSES

A must-have on both menus is horse racing – it's a favourite with the men – they study the racing section in the newspaper, scribble down the names of horses on betting slips, then dash to the bookmakers to place their bets. Afterwards they head home to watch the race on television.

World of Sport have their premium offering at 4pm – wrestling. Wrestling has a strong female following in both television viewing and in wrestling halls.

Grandstand Mains & Dessert

Racing from Ascot

World Cup Skiing from Val Gardena

Boxing from Birmingham*

International Table Tennis from Wigan

International Show Jumping from Olympia

Rugby League Challenge Cup from Wembley

Dessert

Final Score

*Served rare and bloody.

All the above free are from subscription fees, long term contracts and pay-per view charges.

World of Sport mains & Dessert

Superbikes from Donnington
ITV 6 Horse Racing
US Open Golf
Rothmans RAC Open Rally
Speedway from West Germany*
Wrestling from Hull City Hall

Dessert

The Classified Results

*Contains speckles of dirt from racetrack.
Satellite dish installation not required. No hidden charges.

Sport rules on Saturday afternoons. Hundreds of residents are rooted to the sofa, eyes fixed on the television whilst flicking between BBC and ITV. No pay per view or subscriptions needed – the only requirements are a TV, an aerial and a television licence. Simplicity is the name of the game in the province of the Section N Underpass.

CLOSING COMMENTS:

WRESTLING: RISE AND FALL

- In its heyday, wrestling would draw in TV audiences of up to 16 million! Big Daddy and Giant Haystacks were crowd pullers and facing each other smashed audience figures. Big Daddy weighed in at 23 Stone (146 kg) whilst Giant Haystacks was a whopping 40 Stone (254 kg).
- Funnily enough, the decline of wrestling on a Saturday afternoon was partly attributed to the clash between Big Daddy and Giant Haystacks in 1981. After the marathon build up, the bout between the two heavies lasted less than three minutes! Along with the aura of predictability and the shift towards a pantomime, ITV pulled the plug in 1988 (by this time, wrestling had become a standalone programme as World of Sport had ended in 1985). The usual Saturday afternoon of excitement and shouting that wrestling brought into living rooms was replaced with subdued silence. The golden age of wrestling had ended.

- Grandstand was broadcast from 1958 to 2007. The presenters during this time were Peter Dimmock, David Coleman, Frank Bough, Des Lynam and Steve Rider.
- World of Sport was broadcast from 1965 to 1985. The presenters during this time were Eamonn Andrews, Dickie Davies, Fred Dinenage, Steve Rider and Jim Rosenthal.

HOW TO WIN AT MONOPOLY

THE CHEAT SHEET

Max Swain, aged 26, is currently on a winning streak in the board game Monopoly. His winning streak currently spans 47 games, totalling 173 hours. With his Cheshire cat smile and glint in his eye, many of his opponents believe there are mysterious forces behind his wheeling and dealing on the Monopoly board.

The manuscript below sheds light on Max's winning streak. It's believed that the manuscript was drafted by Max and was meant for his friend Julian Jakes. It shows the deceptive thought process adopted by Max – one that flows between the green houses and red hotels on the Monopoly board.

THE CHEAT SHEET

Step 1. Make sure you're the Banker.
Being in the position of the Banker gets you the necessary experience required for handling and swindling money. Being the banker means you can sneakily help yourself to a few £500 notes if things get a bit tight. Every little helps!

Step 2. Portfolio is key.
Competitors will look to snap up those dark blue properties (Park Lane and Mayfair) or the green ones (Bond Street). There's nothing wrong with that train of thought, but think outside the box - ever considered Old Kent Road and Whitechapel? What about the blues of Angel Islington, Euston Road and Pentonville Road? Think about it - if another property tycoon is going through a tough financial time

and has just collected £200 for passing Go, you can swipe that £200 (and more) straight out of their hand if you have three houses on The Angel of Islington. A good mixture of cheap, mid-priced and expensive properties make up a portfolio that will send your competitors into bankruptcy.

Step 3. Jail can be beneficial.
'I've done nothing!' you argue, but you've got to go. You may be in possession of a 'get out of jail free card' but think twice about using it (you can sell it to the highest bidder to top up your cash). A little spell in jail can give you valuable thinking time whilst you take a bit of a break from wheeling and dealing. Once you're out, you'll be shrewder and make your competitors weep as they're whittled down to £1 notes.

Step 4. Don't ignore the Stations!
These stand bang in the centre on each side of the board. They are not yet privatised and are still owned by British Rail. Again, these can be a nice little earner - £50 rent if you have a couple of these stations. Not bad eh?

Step 5. Don't dismiss the Utilities!
Just like the stations the utilities can be a nice little earner. Snap up the Electric Company and Water Works for a bargain of £300 and hope that your competitors land on them … they'll then need to cough up 10 times the amount shown on the dice!

Step 6. Take the rough with the smooth.
Face the fact that you'll get stung at some point when it's your turn to scoop up Chance or Community Chest. You may have to fork out for offences such as speeding and drunk in charge, or maybe your houses are in need of general repairs. The other side of the coin is that you can get tax returns, do well in a beauty contest or even collect a few pounds due to a bank error. It really just comes down to pure luck and you have no say in the matter.
Step 7. Keep on building.

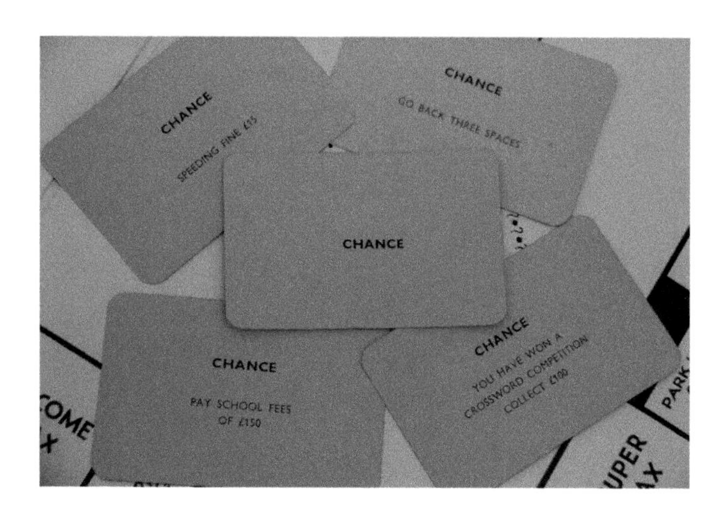

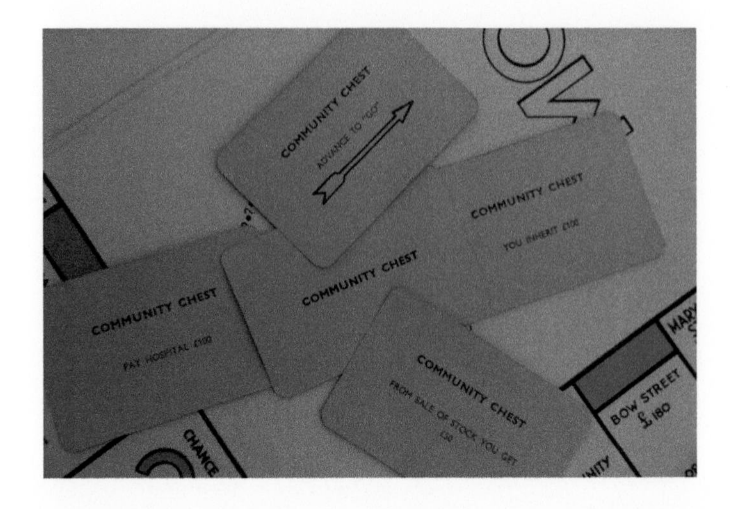

Gobble up as many houses as you can then progress onto hotels. A big red hotel is intimidating for your competitors. Watch them sweat like a pig in a sauna as they approach your stretch of properties. Competitors landing on your hotels could find themselves bankrupt.

Step 8. Keep your eyes peeled!
Sadly there is a lot of dodgy dealings between competitors. In Monopoly there are no regulatory bodies such as the Financial Conduct Authority to keep property tycoons in check, so watch your competitors like a hawk! The only one allowed to cheat in this game is you … the Banker!

Step 9. Be ruthless.
Once a wannabe property tycoon has run out of money and property, kick them out the game! Offer no IOUs or cash - get rid of them!
Step 10. Patience is key.

A game of Monopoly can last for hours so don't be hasty in your decision-making. Set yourself up mentally for a marathon, not a sprint. Stick to these simple steps and you'll be successful in Monopoly and your competitors will be in awe of your shrewdness.

CLOSING COMMENTS:

- Rights to sell Monopoly were acquired by Leeds company Waddingtons in 1935 (from the Parker Brothers).
- Monopoly boards were used by fake charities during World War Two to smuggle maps and messages to prisoners in Nazi occupied Europe. Prisoners of war were allowed to receive cards and board games to relieve boredom. Working in collaboration, Waddingtons and M19 (a branch of the secret service responsible for escape and evasion), printed maps on silk that were laminated within Monopoly boards.
- The character in jail on the board is called 'Jake the Jailbird'.

The Game of
MONOPOLY
Registered Trade Mark
PROPERTY TRADING BOARD GAME
BRIEF IDEA OF THE GAME
The idea of the game is to buy and rent or sell properties so profitably that players increase their wealth — the wealthiest becoming the eventual winner. Starting from "GO", move the tokens around the board according to throw of the dice. When a player's token lands on a space not already owned, he may buy it from the Bank; otherwise it is
CHANCE

SMASH HITS

LESTER DRAKE TALKS TO THE BITCH WITH THE NOTEPAD

Music journalist Wilma Silver appeared on the late night talk show hosted by Lester Drake. Wilma, the self-confessed 'bitch with the notepad', has recently been cleared of assaulting her boyfriend, Robin (drummer for the rock group 'The Speakers'). Wilma and Lester have crossed paths many times over the years. Lester described a previous televised discussion with Wilma as a 'Storm in the Studio'. They cross paths again in this quick televised Q & A session below.

LD: How are you Wilma? What have you been up to since being cleared of assault?

WS: I'm cool. You know shit happens and you just gotta deal with it. It's business as usual - you know me - Wilma Silver - the bitch with the notepad is back!

The studio audience applauds

LD: Good to see that you've not lost the attitude Wilma, and glad you've been cleared of assault, but many think you should have been put behind bars for what you did - stubbing out your cigarette on your boyfriend's penis was pretty cruel - ouch!

Rapturous laughter from the studio audience

WS: It was the second time Robin cheated so what was I supposed to do? He needed to learn that he can't drop his trousers at every opportunity that knocks at his crotch, so he deserved it!

LD: With the court case, and being suspended by your employer, your finances must have taken a steep downward turn?

WS: Not gonna worry about it - now that the court case is done, the cash will come. I'm getting paid for reeling off a load of verbal diarrhoea to you - easy come, easy go. Anyway, I'm not here to discuss my finances.

LD: You have a reputation for carrying lots of cash around - how much money do you have with you tonight - right now?

Wilma pulls out her purse from her back pocket and aims it towards Lester's head. Lester catches it one-handed and the crowd applaud.

WS: I told you not to ask me about money - see for yourself!

She grins as she watches Lester count the coins in the purse

LD: 40p - you have 40p! Wow things are tough - you're gonna have to do lots more interviews and articles to fatten up this purse. How far can you get with just 40p?

WS: Smash Hits - 40p will buy me a copy of Smash Hits. You know about Smash Hits?

LD: Smash Hits music magazine? certainly a popular choice for teenagers - my daughter's bedroom wall is plastered with posters of moody looking pop stars - moody seems to be cool these days. And what about the hairstyles? There's one poster where collectively their hair colours make a complete rainbow!

WS: It's called style and creativity old man - qualities you're severely lacking. Smash Hits is a cool read - the latest edition features The Eurythmics, Soft Cell and Kajagoogoo.

LD: Catagooh?

WS: Kajagoogoo - K-A-J-A-G-O-O-G-O-O. They have a tune out at the moment called 'Too shy'.

LD: Don't think I've heard of them.

WS: Any groups you've heard of?

LD: Buck's Fizz - only because they won the Eurovision song contest years ago. Who else … Bonny Tyler … Thin Lizzy … Madness.

Wilma nods her head in approval

WS: Smash Hits is good - fully dedicated to music - no fighting through 30 pages of bullshit adverts to get to the main articles.

LD: Sounds like a good read - any room for improvement?

WS: Yeah … by me becoming the magazine editor. I'd write shit-hot, slap-you-in-the-face articles that will show I'm not just the bitch with the notepad, I'm also the bitch with brains!

The audience cheers

Lester smiles and gestures to Wilma to catch her purse whilst preparing to toss it back to her

WS: Nah you keep it - it's just loose change.

Wilma pulls out a wad of £20 notes from her back pocket and flashes it arrogantly towards the audience.
The audience roars with laughter and shout 'Wilma, Wilma'.

LD shakes his head in disbelief and smiles

LD: So the after-show drinks are on you then?

WS: Yeah but I'll warn ya, I drink hard and fast and tend to lose my head after a couple bottles of vodka - forgive me if I punch you in the face or smash you over the head with an empty bottle!

CLOSING COMMENTS:

Wilma's current top 10 tunes:

1. Total eclipse of the heart - Bonnie Tyler
2. Sweet dreams (are made of this) – Eurythmics
3. Billie Jean – Michael Jackson
4. Rock the boat – Forrest
5. Africa – Toto
6. Na na hey hey kiss him goodbye – Bananarama
7. Too shy – Kajagoogoo
8. Love on your side – Thompson Twins
9. Speak like a child – Style Council
10. Tomorrow's (just another day) / Madness (is all in the mind) – Madness

- Smash Hits was published fortnightly from 1978 – 2006.
- Sales of the magazine regularly hit 500,000 in the early 1980s.
- The best selling edition featured Kylie Minogue and Jason Donovan – with over one million readers in 1989.

THE NAME IS VIC

HELD CAPTIVE BY THE VIC 20 HOME COMPUTER

Simon Greyhastle, aged 13, has been looking forward to the six-week summer break. He's struggled through the last school term – he finds French painful and maths sends him into mind-numbing boredom. His plan during the six-week summer holiday is to go on day trips to the seaside, visit his grandparents and spend time riding the streets on his Raleigh Chopper. Simon shares his bedroom with a recent birthday present of a Vic 20 home computer – he calls him Vic. Vic is connected to the 14-inch portable television. Simon's competitive personality inherited from his father means that the six-week summer holiday will not go as planned. The invisible handcuffs keeping Simon and Vic together means a summer holiday trapped in a tiny bedroom in the province of the Section N Underpass. In his own words, Simon highlights his intention and addiction …

I wanted the best. The step up was imminent and I'm ready. I know that eventually I'll be able to get to grips with the most powerful home computer on planet earth. I'm filled with excitement and doubt at the prospect of having such power at my fingertips, but I'm ready.

It stands bold and proud. It's the best and he knows this. It's the undisputed, chunky, heavyweight champion of home computers that appeared from nowhere and now stands on the centre podium. His name is Vic.

Time for action. Power on, slide the cassette 'Hoppit' into the cassette player and wait whilst big Vic seeks out the program and loads -up. Success … 'found Hoppit … loading'. I wait with excitement, waiting … waiting. It's ready! I feel the tingle in my fingers as I lean forward and touch the keyboard. The game has begun and I'm the stranded frog who needs to get across a series of busy roads during rush hour. The only way to get across is by skilfully hopping on and off the passing vehicles. If I lose concentration and miss the vehicle, I'm dead! If I'm too slow, I'm dead! Timing, it's all about timing. My finger connection with the keys on the keyboard has to be firm or it's death during rush hour. I carefully judge the speed to the vehicles, then leap! First jump: success. Judge speed and leap again - success. Jump and leap again but I miss the onrushing vehicle and it's a rush hour froggy fatality. The game is generous and has dished out a few more froggy lives to juggle. I keep going … practicing … perfecting the wait-leap-wait sequence.

Vic has changed my life. I'm a hostage in the bedroom, only leaving for food or a toilet break. The days fly by and I don't know which day of the week it is. My only contact with the outside world is waving at the tanned faces of the next-door neighbours through the window. I tell myself I want to get out but Vic holds me hostage with a variety of games. I need him more than he needs me and he knows this.

Be careful of what your heart desires. I wanted that step up and now I'm stuck. It's approaching September and the school term is a few days away. The summer homework is still sitting in the sports bag in the cupboard under the stairs. I think about leaving my bedroom to start tackling the homework, but I can't drag myself away. My excuse for not doing my homework: 'I was held captive by Vic!'

CLOSING COMMENTS:

- The Vic 20 home computer was released in Europe in 1981.
- The original retail selling price was £299.99
- Games were loaded using a cassette player included with the Vic 20 package.

VIC-20
TRAP
GAME CASSETTE
commodore
COMPUTER
VIC-20 TRAP
VIC-20 SPACESNAKE
exceptional software
VIC 20
CHARIOT RACE

VIC-20 TRAP
NO RAM EXPANSION REQUIRED
VIC-20
SPACESNAKE

THE RALEIGH CHOPPER

STRETCHING THE IMAGINATION

CHOPPER

Attendees at the Section N province comprehensive school are encouraged to stretch their imagination. Sarah Gamst, aged 12, proud owner of a Raleigh Chopper, stretches her imagination to the limit as she describes the personality and thoughts of the bicycle.

I am the boss. I'm a natural born leader who stands out from the rest. I was born to lead not follow! I'm like the Queen Bee of bicycles - a lot of the other bicycles serve me and treat me with respect. That's just the way it is - the way it should be - the way I like it.

I have the aura of originality. My design is unique, oozing style and finesse that turns heads wherever I go. I keep myself clean and sharp - shabbiness and poor attention to detail are undesirable traits that I won't accommodate. I'm not Paul Weller but I'm the leader of the Style Council - my name is Chopper.

I have my foes - bicycles that believe they should be the boss. It all comes down to jealously - an unattractive trait that eats away though their aluminium frames like sodium hydroxide. I feel sorry for them - they just don't understand that it's genetics - you're either born with it or not. My leadership quality is natural, born in the heart of Nottingham.

I can't see many bicycles like myself coming through in the future - I'm a rare breed and I'll become a national treasure. My future is bright and even during retirement I'll still be remembered and talked about. My photo will still be splashed inside glossy magazines and cause a commotion. I'm the real deal - pure and undiluted - real, not fake - a legend forever - I am the Raleigh Chopper.

CLOSING COMMENTS:

- The Raleigh Company was established in 1887 in Nottingham.
- The founder, Sir Frank Bowden, discovered his love of cycling after experiencing its health benefits after a spell of being poorly.
- The iconic Chopper was launched in 1970 – 1.5 million of them were sold!

READY BREK

CENTRAL HEATING FOR HARRY

'I can't get out of bed!' – a common grumble for many 14-year-olds. It's typical of them to cover their heads with bedding whilst ignoring the alarm clock and wake-up shouts from their parents. If 14-year-olds ruled the province, crawling out of bed at lunchtime would be acceptable and an Atari 2600 would be a school replacement! Luckily they don't rule the province, they do have to get out of bed in the mornings and the games consoles are only permitted after school.

For many pupils, the walk to school can be painful – especially in the depth of winter. In this story, the journey to school is less painful for 14-year-old Harry Greyleader. Harry's choice of Ready Brek for breakfast ensures he's well prepared for the challenging tasks ahead.

LYONS
original
Ready
Brek

He pulls the front door shut and steps out into the mist on the way to school. The mist engulfs him but his glow is evident. Minutes later, looking like a youthful group of Reservoir Dogs, a pack of eight pupils is formed. Harry is comfortable wherever he is in the pack - at the front, middle or hanging back, it makes no difference. He listens to the weekend chatter and nods in acknowledgement. The chatter is relentless and he chips in with 'how' and 'why' whilst making sense of it all.

There's a break in the weekend chatter as members of the pack break off to grab fuel - breakfast on the go. The weekend chatter wears thin as focus is shifted to wolfing the fuel down. He's the only one who didn't need to stop to pick-up breakfast on the go.

The decibels increase as school gets closer. Members of the pack are displaced and replaced. The chatter subjects flip like a frantic game of snap, but he manages to keep pace.

Inside the classroom and it's time to take it all in. He's ready and focused - warm and comfortable.

Many have spoken about Ready Brek, the hot oat cereal. His parents swore by it and now he's followed in their footsteps. It tastes good. Unlike the complicated equations scribbled on the board, the hot oat cereal is simple. Little by little he's able to unscramble the cryptic equations but they keep coming. Like a series of locked doors, unpick the next lock only to find another one. He's still focused and eventually it all makes sense.

A successful maths lesson was helped by his well-executed start - Ready Brek. Onto the next lesson, English - his glow is still evident as he takes his seat in the classroom.

CLOSING COMMENTS:

- Ready Brek oat cereal was originally launched in 1957 and celebrated its 60th birthday in 2017.
- Many consumers still fondly remember the 'Central heating for kids' strapline.
- 56 bowls of Ready Brek are bought every minute and is bought by nearly 2 million shoppers every year!

MY PREFERRED CHOICE OF WEAPON

BY MRS J. HASTINGS

SCHOOL days. Many call them the best days of their lives. Memories of a carefree life, weird hairstyles, some of the best and worst teachers come flooding back. In the 60s, 70s and 80s, school discipline was very different compared to school discipline now. Miss J. Hastings, teacher at Bunting High School, 1960 – 1980, describes how she dished out punishment during her teaching career.

Some of my colleagues would deliver a swift slap to the ear or use a wooden ruler to crack the knuckles.

There was one weapon of punishment, which stood head and shoulders above the rest - the board eraser! The board eraser was my preferred choice of weapon.

Initially I struggled to make an impact when launching the eraser - my throwing technique was poor and fell short of my target resulting in giggles from the pupils. The giggles persisted but my colleagues encouraged me to keep trying. The turning point came in September 1966. School had re-opened after the summer break. It had been a fantastic summer - England had won the football World Cup and many of the kids were still in holiday mode. It was during the geography lesson that things came to a head. I heard whispering and giggling whilst I jotted down a few key points about land erosion on the board. It all happened so quickly - I spun round 180 degrees and launched the eraser with venom. It flew through the air like a missile and hit his cheek … I'd hit my target! There were gasps around the classroom as my target massaged his reddened cheek. That was the turning point. After that first successful hit, many others followed and I guess I gained a reputation. The behaviour of my pupils improved. I even overheard pupils muttering 'Missile Hastings' as I walked along the corridor.

CLOSING COMMENTS:

How could something so innocent cause so much pain? How could something that's used to remove chalk from the board behave like a highly developed missile? How did teachers learn to launch such a missile and ensure it hit its target?

It's astonishing how, with their backs to the class, teachers would know which pupil to target, calculate the distance, twist 180 degrees and launch the eraser with the exact amount of force to hit their target. Miss J. Hastings, former teacher at Bunting High, is now retired. She spends her days catching up with friends and reminiscing about her teaching career. She also enjoys the peacefulness of relaxing in her armchair, only the clashing of knitting needles breaking the silence as she makes pieces of clothing for her grandchildren.

THREE POPULAR PUNISHMENTS FROM YESTER-YEARS WERE:

1. *The cane on the bum*
2. *A ruler, old footwear (slipper, shoe, football boot) or cane across the palm of the hand*
3. *Twisting of the ear until the pupil shrieked whilst in a lopsided position*

Luckily corporal punishment was abolished in English state schools in 1986 and in 1998 for independent sector schools!

IAN'S SURVIVAL PLAN WHILST AT GRANGE HILL

Ian Autumntree, aged 48, was a huge fan of Grange Hill. He holds fond memories of the characters of the popular children's TV series. Ian was asked how he would survive a term at Grange Hill – what tactics he would use to ensure he made it through a term unscathed. He was also asked about his GH crushes.

> The first thing I'd do is find allies and know my enemies. I'd certainly get in with Tucker Jenkins and his crew of Benny and Alan. Tucker is cheeky and always ducking and diving. I've had numerous tricky situations throughout my life so Tucker would be my boy manoeuvring me to safety. I'd describe Tucker as the artful dodger of Grange Hill - skilful and sometimes cunning.

BRM-M
PH-HEW!
BIFF
BASH!

Sports teacher Geoff 'Bullet' Baxter may be firm but he's also fair. He's got a listening ear and will take my concerns to heart. Behind that hard man image is a teacher who actually cares about your wellbeing - like a Fry's chocolate cream, hard on the outside but soft in the middle. Baxter gets the thumbs up from me.

One guy I'd avoid is Gripper Stepson - I wouldn't want to be beaten like a piece of steak being tenderised with a mallet! I guess one way to avoid getting beaten up by him is to join him - if you can't beat 'em then join 'em! Personally I'm not hard-hearted enough to turn someone upside down and shake their dinner money from their pockets. Gripper Stepson - bloody hell he's a nasty piece of work!

I like Zammo - he's a likeable guy - he's always smiling but such a shame he found a new friend - heroin! I wouldn't avoid Zammo and I'd acknowledge him with a nod of the head but that's where my involvement ends. I wouldn't lend him any money or accompany him to any after school activities. A good guy attracted to the wrong company - a real shame.

I'd certainly distance myself from Mr Bronson. If I were to get a major ear bashing from him, I'd just stand there and suck it up without giving off any backchat. I know that if I gave off any backchat he'd let rip with a verbal assault comparable to an M16 rifle - best to accept it and protect the eardrums for another day. After all, I wouldn't want my term turning into turmoil!

Imelda Davis was brutal - I once saw her shove glass fibre down someone's back. I wouldn't want to be sliced into segments like a Terry's Chocolate Orange so I'd keep clear of Imelda! She'll not only smash-up the other girls but the guys too! I don't fancy any of what Imelda is dishing out. You might be considering which is worse … being taken apart by Imelda or battered by Gripper? They're both pretty much on a par!

I'd be smart in Mrs McClusky's office. There may be situations where Tucker may not come up trumps and I'll get dragged to her office to be disciplined. The thing with McClusky is that she works on the principal of guilty until proven innocent - she's the jury and judge in the courtroom within the walls of Grange Hill. It's your call whether to lie or not, but if lying means surviving the term without getting my head shoved down the toilet then I'd lie! I'd make sure my story was watertight before entering her courtroom. The bottom line is I'd do what's needed to survive.

I fancied quite a few of the Grange Hill girls. Even Imelda could have been a bit of a looker if she had got rid of the vicious streak. In no particular order, here are the girls I adored:

Trish Yates
Cathy Hargreaves
Claire Scott
Fay Lucas
Calley Donnington
Jackie Wright
Annette Firman

CLOSING COMMENTS:

- GH was an incredibly popular BBC TV series with characters that are still remembered.
- The gates of GH opened in February 1978 and closed in September 2008.
- Peter 'Tucker' Jenkins appeared in GH from 1978 – 1982 and was played by Todd Carty. Tucker was such a popular character that the spin-off, Tucker's Luck, was aired from 1983 to 1985. Tucker's Luck followed Tucker and his mates ducking and diving during a time of high unemployment. Tucker made an appearance in the last episode of GH in 2008.

- Gripper Stepson was played by Mark Savage. Gripper terrorised pupils from 1980 to his expulsion in 1983.
- GH didn't hold back when it came to social issues. Viewers were gripped by the storyline of Zammo's heroin addiction – the shocking scene of Zammo slumped in the toilet after overdosing is still remembered. The storyline led to the 'just say no' campaign. Zammo Maguire was played by Lee MacDonald.
- Mr Bronson was played by Michael Sheard.
- Imelda Davis was played by Fleur Taylor
- Geoff 'Bullet' Baxter was played by Michael Cronin
- Mrs McClusky was played by Gwyneth Powell

THE ALLEGRO, THE AMBASSADOR, SEL THE MECHANIC AND CASTROL MOTOR OIL

Below lies a testimony from Danny Smalls. Danny is a big fan of car makers British Leyland and currently owns an Austin Ambassador. He still relies on the services of Sel the mechanic to keep the Ambassador in tip-top condition.

> My Allegro was kept in top condition thanks to Mindful Motors Garage (MMG). I didn't like taking it to any other garage as once got stung when I did - they charged a fortune and didn't even do a tyre pressure check! MMG's owner and mechanic, Sel, is a top bloke. He always does a good job and I can trust him not to take the Allegro out for a thrashing during his lunch break. Now the Allegro has gone, Sel now services my Ambassador. I know British

Leyland have a bit of a reputation for making not very reliable cars, but my Allegro and new Ambassador have been trouble-free, all thanks to Sel.

The Allegro had a 1.3 litre engine and a top speed of 78 mph. Naught to 60 took 20 seconds. I remember seeing the advert on television, 'The Allegro, the new driving force from Austin', nipping to the showroom and falling in love with it. I shelled out £1,150. The Allegro lasted six years before I sold it and got the Ambassador. The Ambassador has a top speed of 96 mph and naught to 60 takes 14.2 seconds. It was also much more pricey than the Allegro – £5,100! The price tag was not a major issue as I've landed a senior position in the company and become a 'big cheese' – the silver name plaque on my office door means I fit the Ambassador like a glove – executive status at work and on the road.

The key to keeping the cars in tip-top condition was a regular oil change – every 6,000 miles for the Ambassador. Sel always used Castrol – I've never seen him use any other brand to be honest. He'd say that 10w40 grade would keep the Ambassador running smooth.

I love the Ambassador but it's a shame that British Leyland stopped making 'em after only two years in production. I'll keep driving my Ambassador until it dies – but I must say, at this rate, with the combination of Sel and Castrol, I can see myself being buried long before Ambassador is brought into the scrapyard!

© Castrol Ltd

A million good reasons for using Castrol GTX.
95,000
230,000
151,000
180,000
259,000
200,000
Six cars. A million miles between them.
6 cars. Over a million miles on the clock between them. And each one without a rebore. Quite a tribute to their owners. And to the oil they all use. Castrol GTX.
Take a tip from the experts on long engine life. Regular servicing with Castrol GTX gives you better protection, adds up to more miles per car. Isn't that what real economy's all about?
Team up with Castrol GTX–and enjoy a lot more mileage on the great road ahead.
bp
With Castrol GTX at heart, there's a
GTX

© Castrol Ltd

CLOSING COMMENTS:

- Castrol was founded by Charles Wakefield in 1899 under the name 'CC Wakefield & Company'.
- Initially the company sold lubricants for trains and heavy machinery.
- Charles took a keen interest in the automobile and airplane industry. The company developed lubricants for these sectors that were runny enough to work from cold during start-ups, and thick enough to keep working at high temperatures. The company was able to achieve this by adding castor oil to their formula. The new product was called 'Castrol'.
- The Castrol name appeared (via sponsorship) on banners and flags at aviation events and auto races.
- In 1960, CC Wakefield & Company simply became 'Castrol Ltd'.

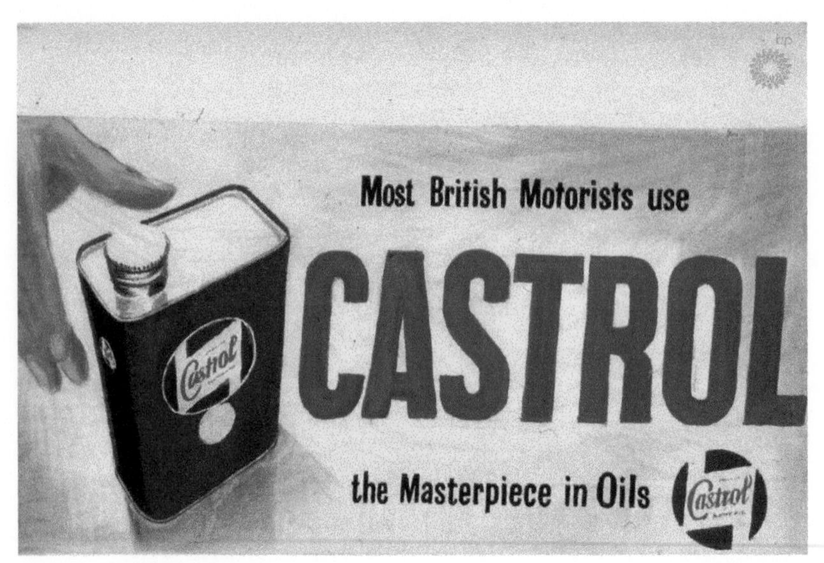

© Castrol Ltd

THE ALLEGRO, THE AMBASSADOR, SEL THE MECHANIC
AND CASTROL MOTOR OIL

THE FORD CAPRI

A SHORT TALE OF A REGRETFUL TAXI DRIVER

Jack Remolsen remembers the Ford Capri – one of his all time favourite cars. He considers himself unlucky not to have owned one. There's a look of happiness and sadness as Jack reminisces over the Capri owned by his older brother. Memories and regrets from the province of the Section N Underpass.

It was yellow and I still remember the registration plate: MGP 119P. You couldn't mess with this motor. It stood out from the rest - sporty, swift and it turned heads. How could you resist its sporty looks, sleek design and awesome power? The long bonnet is iconic!

How can I remember the registration plate after so many years? I never forget a car that stands out from the crowd. That Capri really stood out boldly (especially since it was yellow). My eldest brother was the proud owner of this classy car. Other cars were gunning for the Capri but eventually they'd hang their heads in defeat. The Capri was just unique.

He's sporty … Daley Thompson on four wheels - powerful, muscular, flexible, and a crowd pleaser. A competitor and winner - he's first to the finishing line and scoops-up the gold medal.

All Capri's looked stunning - I'd see them outside the latest trendy hangouts as I dropped off the rich and famous.

I remember Bodie and Doyle from The Professionals jumping into the Capri and speeding off to deal with villains. They also used it whilst dating the ladies. The Capri is action-packed with a smooth and charming personality.

My brother decided to go for the bigger, less sporty car and offered me the Capri for 200 quid. I thought the price tag was a bit steep so I refused to buy it. He instead sold it to his friend, who in turn ran it into the ground. It was last seen on a nearby street being held up with bricks. A sad end to an iconic legend. Looking back, I wish I hadn't been such a tight-arse and forked out the 200 quid - I would have cherished that motor! I often look out at my uninspiring car on the driveway and think if only I could swap it for a Capri. Of course there's a few up for sale but the sellers are asking silly money … a lot more than 200 quid!

When you mention iconic cars, the Capri will be on the list. Dynamic and sporty, fast and furious, smooth and elegant, bold and confident - the Capri.

CLOSING COMMENTS:

- The Capri was the European version of the Mustang – it was to be a car that was sporty and appealed to young people.
- Production of the Capri began in 1968 in Halewood, Liverpool and also in Germany.
- The Capri was marketed as 'the car you always promised yourself'.
- The final production of the Capri was in November 1986.

THE GREEN CROSS CODE MAN

THE HELPLESS GENT

The Green Cross Code Man – a gentle gent who puts our safety first. His body language indicates frustration – new arrivals into the province updating him on the chaos on the streets: pedestrians crossing roads whilst using portable telephones, pedestrians wearing headphones and not bothering to stop, look and listen. The Green Cross Code Man holds up his imaginary white flag – he feels helpless stuck in the province of the Section N Underpass. Searching for a catapult to hurl himself out of the province has been fruitless. Below is one of the many frustrating reports that he's received from new arrivals.

Use the Green Cross code

I watched him daydreaming whilst striding down the street - probably thinking about dinner and what to buy at the supermarket. He's chatting on his portable telephone whilst heading towards the supermarket when suddenly his stride is brought to an abrupt halt by the screech of tyres on tarmac. In the middle of a road, he glances down at the car … there's a two inch difference between him and the bonnet and the traffic light is glaring green! The driver, who almost wiped him out, compliments him on his skills of observation, each descriptive word beginning with 'f'. The driver then screams 'USE THE GREEN CROSS CODE YOU WALLY!' before driving off.

Stop, Look and Listen - he didn't do any of these so he was a few inches away from disaster. You would have thought that he'd be embarrassed by his lackadaisical action - he wasn't - in fact he angrily gave the driver the 'V' sign with his fingers then continued his conversation on his mobile telephone! I watched as he then almost wiped-out an old lady whilst pulling a shopping trolley from the stack and spinning it around - all this whilst still on his portable telephone!

CLOSING COMMENTS

- The Green Cross Code was a road safety campaign that began in 1970. It was characterised by the Green Cross Code Man and the straplines 'Stop, Look and Listen' and 'always use the green cross code'. The campaign was aimed at helping children cross roads safely.

JOHN STONEYLEIGH-SMITH IS THE VOICE OF ACCESS

YOUR FLEXIBLE FRIEND

The sales pitch – some people have the amazing gift of persuasion. John Stoneyleigh-Smith has quickly become one the most recognisable voices on television. His distinctive, fun, energetic tone captivates audiences living in the province of the Section N Underpass. Below is the swift sales pitch John uses – a sales pitch used to promote the Access Card, a new and flexible way to purchase items whilst out and about. The television advert is shown between the hours of 6pm and 10pm. John Stoneyleigh-Smith & the Access Card – a captivating partnership well known to hundreds of viewers living in the province of the Section N Underpass.

Access Advertising Autumn 1981

These days it's all uphill for money.

Let Access pitch in with your bills and the high street shopping.

It can be used anytime. Anywhere. Access is your flexible service and welcome at thousands of outlets throughout the UK and all over the world.

So if you're over 18 and would like to know more about Access, call into any of the banks listed below.

You never know, Access could be giving your money a helping hand in the months to come.

GIVE MONEY A HELPING HAND.

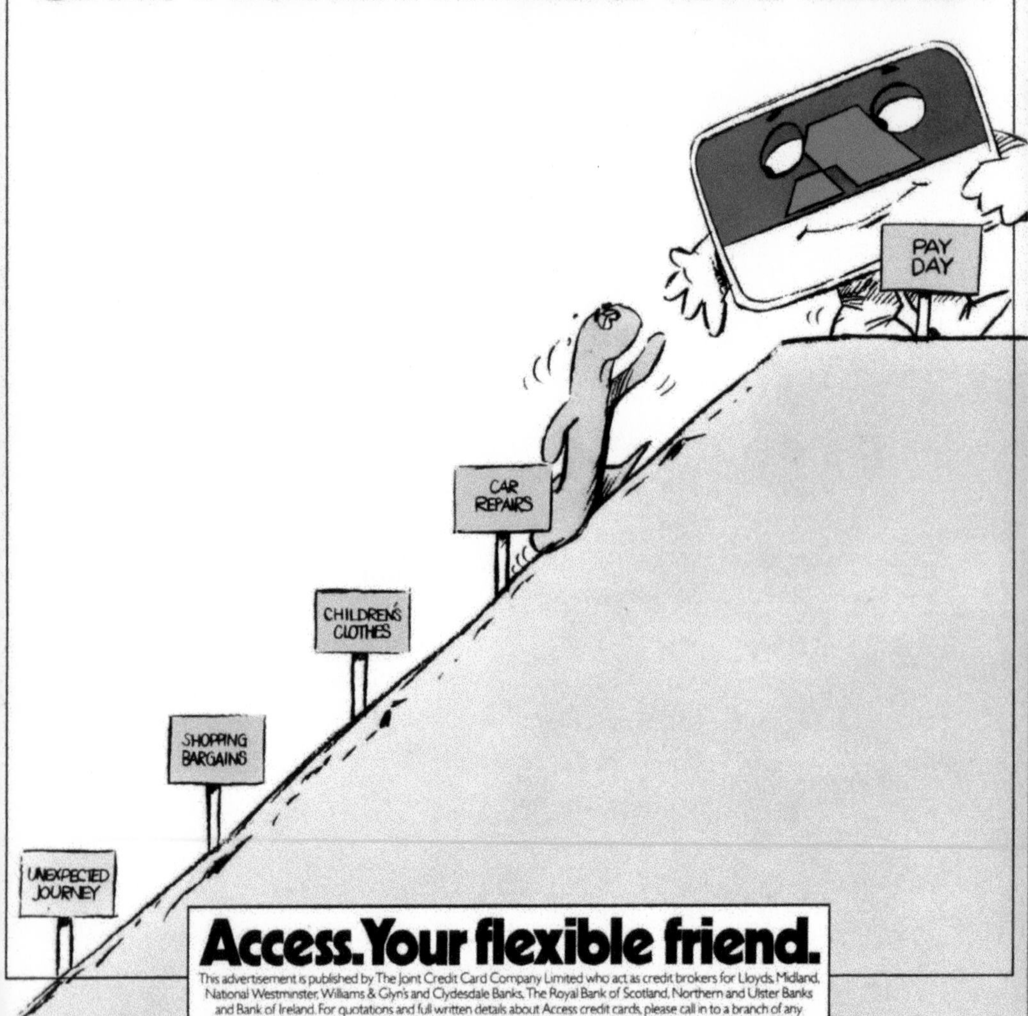

Carrying lots of hard cash around can be like going for a tedious run around the block - painful and sweaty. I've seen guys with their trousers almost down to their knees due to the weight of their wallet. I've also seen women with lopsided shoulders because of the weight of cash in their handbags.

Some weight relief is needed so let's kick bulky wallets and falling down trousers into touch! We don't want to see women looking like the leaning tower of Pisa. The answer to the weighty cash problem is the Access Card!

Leave the cash in the bank and slip the access card in your wallet or purse. You'll feel the difference straight away - less stress on the heart and trousers. You'll be walking as straight as a freshly trained soldier!

The access card makes things so easy. Need to fill up on some four-star leaded fuel? Pull out the Access Card and pay easily and swiftly. Drive off chuffed that you didn't need to fight through a wad of notes.

Seen a nice piece of jewellery that you can't resist? Flick out the Access Card and snap it up! Walk away with a huge smile knowing the battle of the bulging purse didn't happen.

The Access Card will change your life forever. No more making sure you have a chequebook and guarantee card before you head to the shops. Simplicity is the name of the game and the Access Card is all about keeping life simple. The Access Card is your no nonsense, space saving, lightweight, reliable friend. Embrace and enjoy the Access Card.

CLOSING COMMENTS

- The first credit card to be launched in the UK was the Barclaycard in 1963.
- The Access Card was launched on 23 October 1972. The banks that launched Access were Lloyds Bank, Midland Bank, National Westminster Bank and the Royal Bank of Scotland/Williams

& Glyn's group. The aim of the credit card was twofold: 1) to provide an alternative and simple way to transmit money and 2) to make available a limited form of revolving credit to cardholders without the complexities associated with other forms of personal credit.

- The strapline used in advertising, 'Access – your flexible friend' was seen in newspapers, magazines and on television.

A BRIEF HISTORY OF BRITISH TELECOM TOLD

BY EASTENDER SCOTT MANNING

DIAL

BUSBY

Scott Manning talks about the changes in communication. Scott and his wife Penny live a merry life in the province of the Section N Underpass. Scott gives us a rundown of how BT forged ahead in the world of communications and how new technology frightened the living daylights out of him!

Vocabulary required to fully understand Scott:

Ball and chalk: walk

Battlecruiser: boozer, pub

Geezer: guy or man

A laugh n a joke: to smoke

Dog and bone: telephone

Vera Lyn: Gin

da: the

Kick and Prance: dance

Bees and honey: money

Apples and Pears: stairs

Scarpered: leave, depart or flee

Lionel Blairs: flairs, trousers

'allway: hallway

Cor blimey: Goodness gracious!

Scarpered: dash-off, leave, disappeared

'ousing: housing

Give 'em a buzz – call someone on the telephone

Old man: dad

Brown bread: dead

Skin and blister: sister

Khyber pass: arse, backside, bum

Claws: fingernails

Frog and toad: road

Raspberry tart: fart, to break wind

Loaf of bread: head

Adam and Eve: believe

'aving a bubble bath: having a laugh, unbelievable

Todd Sloan: alone

Trouble and Strife: wife

A visit to the telephone box
Meant a short ball and chalk,
To the geezer next door
Who bit his claws.
I'd ask him:
'Can I use your dog and bone?'
He'd always say Yes
I'd leave the 2p on his desk.
After the call, I'd show my appreciation for his kindness with 'Cheers geezer - see ya later'.

My old man had some bees and honey
We got our own dog and bone,
Proudly sat on the 'allway table
Cor blimey we were chuffed.

Friends scarpered to smaller cities
Cheap 'ousing drawing them afar,
The dog and bone our saviour
A gift we'll always savour.

A yellow bird appeared
Buzby was his name,
His motto was 'Make someone happy - give 'em a buzz'
His advice music to me ears
I ended up chatting for years.

Cor blimey those bills were huge
My old man was angry,
I was almost brown bread

Until I screamed out loud
'It was my skin and blister!'
A bit of thinking fast,
Saved my Khyber Pass!
The phone box on the street
Still popular it was,
But if the sky rockets are empty
Without a coin or two
What do you do?
Whilst out and about without a doubt
The phone card helped me out.

Buzby was booming
New dog and bones connected
But I sensed something ahead
A kick up the arse to move us fast
And right I was with my inkling.

The computer shoved the typewriter
Into the scrapyard it fell
But we didn't hear the bell!

New technology arrived,
Many of us cried!
Portable telephones hit the streets
Beeping text messages hurt me head
And dial-up internet crackled.
The magic of email emerged
Amazed by all this technology
But how was I going to cope?
Fear of change tangled my stomach,
A raspberry tart rang out.

My loaf of bread was spinning
I couldn't quite Adam and Eve it
But my grand-daughter said 'it's here to stay'
And taught me the technological ways.
I'll always remember,
Her lessons in December.

I'm happy here in the province
Glad I'm not Todd Sloan
Trouble and strife is never far away
But happy and settled we are.

Evenings in the battlecruiser
A laugh n a joke with a few Vera Lyns,
Kick and prance to the music.

Up the apples and pears
Off with the Lionel Blairs
Too much booze makes the body loose,
Time to rest my head in bed.

Out for the count in seconds,
Dreams of our old life
We're thankful for the detour
That brought us to the province.
Resting assured I do
Knowing if we ever return
We'll still remember,
Those lessons in December.

CLOSING COMMENTS:

- The first phone book was issued on 15 January 1880. It contained 248 person and business names without telephone numbers. Callers need to call the exchange and ask to be connected the person or business listed in the phone book. In 1896 the first phone book for the whole country was published – it contained 1,350 pages and 81,000 entries.
- Nationalisation of the telephone service meant it was controlled by the Post Office (1912). The telephone service continued to operate under the postmaster general until 1969 when the Post Office became a public corporation. The British Telecommunication Act 1981 came into force and British Telecom was transferred to private ownership – this meant that telecommunications activity separated from the Post Office. Privatisation of British Telecom took place in 1984.
- There were 267 telephone kiosks (boxes) in 1922 – by 1982 there were 72,415!
- Phone cards were launched in 1981. Sales of phone cards were as high as 74 million in 1991!

MATEY TO THE RESCUE

The letter of praise below was received by the consumer department of the Section N Cosmetic, Beauty and Laundry Company. It was written and sent in by Mrs R Raven. She explains how bath times have become enjoyable for her son James.

29 Beech Street
Charndales Town
Section N Province
SNP1 0PX

12 June 2017

Dear Sir or Madam,

I thought I would send you this short letter to say thank you for making bath times enjoyable for my five-year-old son, James.

matey
NEW
LIQUID
matey*
BBLES CHILDREN CLEAN
they play in the

Prior to using Matey, it was murder trying to get James into the bath – he'd scream, cry and wriggle around like a possessed octopus when I tried lifting him into it. On the few occasions I managed to get him in, he'd get so wound-up and end up angrily splashing the water on the floor and all over me! The whole bathtime business was stressful and the bathroom lino became a slip hazard.

It was whilst I was doing the weekly shop in Safeway that I saw Matey bubble bath on the shelf. I though I'd might as well give it a try, so I bought a bottle.

That evening, I poured some Matey into the running bath. I shouted 'Bath time!' and straight away I heard him kicking off, saying 'I'm not having a bath!' His father got an elbow in the eye as he lifted James up and carried him upstairs into the bathroom. The screaming from James' lungs was unbearable as his father struggled to keep hold of him. Then something supernatural happened – the bathroom became silent and the wriggling stopped as James fixed his eyes on the bath full of bubbles. After his father had put him down, James quickly undressed himself and I lifted him into the bath.

Thirty minutes later he was all smiles and giggles! In fact he wanted to stay in for longer and keep playing with his rubber ducks but I noticed his fingers began shrivelling like prunes, so I convinced him to come out. Since then every bathtime has been a non-challenging experience.

Thank you Matey! No more bathtime tantrums or treading gingerly over the soaking wet lino!

Yours sincerely,

A calm and dry Mrs R Raven.

CLOSING COMMENTS:

- Matey was launched in 1958.
- The characters Matey the sailor, Max, Molly and Pegleg appeared on the bottles.
- The strapline for Matey in the 1970s adverts was 'Clean fun, Clean kids, Clean bath'.

THE BIG CLEAN-UP WITH JUDY JACOBSON

'A clean house eliminates embarrassment!' – a saying made famous by Judy Jacobson, host of television programme 'Shift that Grime'. Residents of the Section N province have the opportunity to express their cleaning challenges by writing into the show – if successful, Judy would go round and give it a good clean whilst dishing out hints and tips. The requirement to appear on the show is the desire to have a home that's not embarrassing to unexpected guests. Below Judy gives a brief recollection of when she visited the home of Jill and Simon Kenrardy.

> Things didn't look bad at all in the hallway – in fact it looked reasonably clean and tidy. Things took a turn for the worse when they showed me the kitchen. How should I describe the state of the cooker … repainted with

numerous splatterings of dried up food - I even noticed an insect munching away at a splattering! 'We kept putting off the cleaning until it's become like this - we had all the intention of doing it but it's just become unmanageable' was Simon's reply when I asked how the cooker had got into such a state. The stickiness of the floor tried to halt my steps as I walked across to the pile of washing up in the sink. Upstairs in the bathroom, I was engulfed by the stench of stale towels and a stale urine smell from the toilet. Immediate action was needed so I dashed outside to my car and grabbed my cleaning kit.

My cleaning kit contains the following:

4 pairs of marigold gloves
2 rectangular bowls
Mop and bucket
1 bottle of Domestos
1 bottle of Jif
1 bottle of Sqezy
Pack of 5 cleaning sponges
10 cleaning cloths
1 box of Persil Automatic

Back in the house, the camera crew took their positions and I got to work. With my marigolds on, I squirted some Jif onto the cooker. I had a bowl of hot water close-by so I was rubbing, rinsing the cloth, and then rubbing again. It

Reproduced with kind permission of Unilever from an original in Unilever Archives

took quite a lot of elbow grease and a few more squirts of Jif to shift the layers of dried-on mess but the result was a ‘like new’ cooker. After emptying the bowl of mucky water, it was onto the pile of washing up.

Jill explained that every time she took out a plate from the cupboard, or piece of cutlery from the draw, they were sprinkled with random bits of dried-on food. As the cameras shifted closer towards her, she embarrassedly admitted that she was at a 'dead end' and didn't know what to do. Before loading the pile of plates and cluster of cutlery into the sink, I filled it with hot water and added a dash of Sqezy washing up liquid. I left them soaking to loosen the dried-on food debris and went upstairs to tackle the bathroom.

In the bathroom, Jill and Simon got stuck in. Jill used a damp cloth and Jif to tackle the bath and tiles whilst Simon gave the toilet a good once over. He applied the finishing touch to the toilet by pouring a generous dose of Domestos bleach around the inside of the bowl. We then scooped up the pile of dirty towels and took them downstairs to the washing machine.

Back in the kitchen, they enthusiastically finished off the washing up - the food debris falling away easily with a gentle bit of rubbing after the soak. Simon mopped the floor (a dash of Sqezy in a bucket works wonders on floors) and Jill loaded the towels into the washing machine and added a couple of scoops of Persil Automatic washing powder in the detergent drawer.

The transformation of the kitchen and bathroom was incredible. Having arrived four hours earlier finding the Kenrardy's downbeat and hopeless, we were leaving them grateful, happy and encouraged. More importantly, they were in a position to openly invite guests into their home without embarrassment. 'A clean house eliminates embarrassment!'

CLOSING COMMENTS

- Jif arrived in the UK in 1974 (it had been available in France since 1969 but was called Cif). The advertising focused on how some powders can 'scratch like skates on ice' but Jif 'cleans through to the shine' without scratching. The name Jif was changed to Cif in 2001.
- In 1956, Sqezy was the first washing up liquid to be sold in the UK in a squeezable plastic container. It inspired the slogan 'Easy peasy lemon Sqezy'.
- Domestos began in the Newcastle garden shed of William Handley in 1929. William sold sodium hypochlorite solution as a steriliser, drain cleaner and for the treatment of sore feet! Originally Domestos was sold door to door but became available through retail outlets in 1952. This was when the slogan, 'kills all known germs ... dead!' was first coined.
- Persil was the world's first soap powder with a bleaching agent! In was developed in 1903 by Professor Herman Giessler and Dr Herman Bauer in Stuttgart, Germany. Persil was launched in the UK as the 'Amazing Oxygen Washer' in 1909.

BRUT AFTERSHAVE

HOMME DE FRANCE WITH ATTITUDE

Retiree Michael Stringers recalls Saturday nights out. He talks about his grooming regime that includes Brut aftershave. Now happily retired, the rumbling machines in the factory have been replaced with buzzing bees and a light breeze rustling through the leaves whilst relaxing in the hammock in the garden. The interview rubber-stamps the theory that the power of advertising, along with the great smell of Brut aftershave, shows no signs of slowing down within the province of the Section N Underpass.

after shave,
after shower,
after anything...
FABERGE
BRUT
FOR MEN
BRUT
The bold invigorating
fragrance for men created by
Fabergé

Q: Describe the build-up to a Saturday night out.
A: After the excitement of the horse racing, it was time to think about the night out. It was about how much cash was in the wallet - maybe you'd had a lucky day on the horses and were able to really splash the cash. Saturday nights meant getting spruced up - making sure you were well dressed. It all started in the bathroom - a hot bath, soap on a rope, loading a new blade into the razor and having a shave - I'd finish off with a splash of Brut. Then we'd head to The Grand Junction Arms looking good and smelling good.

Q: Grand Junction Arms … a pub?
A: Yes a pub on the Grand Union canal - near the railway bridge. I'd get there for about nine and start with a pint of Harp beer. A few of the blokes from the factory were usually in so I'd have a chat with them. A few games of darts and a bit of banter meant we forgot about the rumbling machines in the busy factory.

Q: Why Brut? There were other aftershaves available so why Brut in particular?
A: Most of the other guys wore Brut. It was the first choice of aftershave for many of us. My wife, Doreen, loves it! She described it as a manly aftershave. Brut is a regular in the bathroom cabinet. It's an aftershave that just works for all occasions - I splashed it

on when Doreen and I got married and numerous other events over the years - christenings, parties, funerals - Brut aftershave has been there for all occasions. I wore it to numerous events over the years - weddings, christenings, funerals - name the occasion, Brut's been there.

Q: So why so loyal and captivated by Brut?
A: It smelt good! The advertising was fun too. I loved watching Henry Cooper in those TV adverts. I remember Barry Sheene doing a few of the ads too - 'Splash it all over!' was the strapline. They say 'you can't beat the great smell of Brut' and I agree with that statement.

Q: If Brut were a person, what kind of personality would he have?
A: He'd be brutally honest - the sort of guy who'd give you a couple of slaps around the face and tell you to man up! He'd take no nonsense from anyone - homme de France with attitude!

Q: Did you try any other aftershaves?
A: I stuck to Brut to be honest - I like it, my wife likes it, so no real reason to chop and change.

CLOSING COMMENTS

- Famous sporting personalities and snappy straplines meant Brut appealed to thousands of men.
- Brut men's fragrance brand was launched in 1964 by Fabergé Perfumes (Paris).
- In 1973, Brut was relaunched as Brut 33 – the 33 represented the product still contained 33% of the original fragrance.
- Brut was endorsed by Henry Cooper (British heavyweight boxer) and Barry Sheene (motorcycle racer).

MAXWELL HOUSE COFFEE

Sitting with his back against the twin tub initially felt comfortable – the heat setting was just right providing the kind of comfort felt when you jump into a cold bed with a hot water bottle, but the utility room door had swung back to the closed position and the heat is now unbearable. Carlton is quarter-way through the documents in the shoebox but the heat generated by the twin tub feels like his internal organs are slowly being poached. The smell, a blend of boiling clothes and hot washing powder has irritated his nostrils causing regular sniffles and the occasional sneeze. 'Never sit in one position for too long' – the advice from the physiotherapist comes to mind as he gingerly gets to his feet. The kitchen is much cooler. Take two – lighting the hob with a Swan Vesta match and putting the kettle back onto to boil. In the yellow larder pantry unit he finds a glass container of Maxwell House coffee. He quickly finds the cups, teaspoons, milk and sugar cubes. The coffee is magic in a teacup – it provides instant relief and brings the sniffles and sneezes to a halt. Back into the living room with the cup of coffee – the time on the flip clock is 11:56. Recollection of the morning so far – first cup of coffee at 7.30am – caught the train at 8 – led out the tunnel at about 8.45 – dropped off by the taxi at 9.20 – finally plucked up the courage to put the front door key into the lock and enter the house after hesitating for ten minutes.

He considers his new life in the province. If those documents in the shoebox are anything to go by then life could be reasonably good. Escape was the first thing on his mind when he arrived in the region but now he's in two minds – the car loan, the outstanding balance of £28,000 spread over three credit cards, the chunky mortgage for the simple one bedroom apartment and the stormy on-off relationship with Jess. The province could be a fresh start.

The ring on the doorbell startles him, sending a stream of coffee down his wrist. After placing the cup on the coffee table, Carlton cautiously makes his way to the front door. 'Hello Duck – I noticed that you've recently moved in and wanted to make you feel welcome in the village. I'm Sandra – I live just down the road. And your name is? Actually why don't you come over to our place for a cup of tea and some manor house cake so I can find out lots about you?'

He feels Sandra's eyes checking out every detail of the hallway as he heads back to the living room to get the front door key. No sign of the key in the living room, so he retraces his tracks and bingo, it's on the kitchen worktop. Meeting Sandra in the living room makes him jump – 'Sorry Duck, I was just taking a look around – sounds like the previous tenants have left the washer on – I'll go and quickly sort it'. They leave the house five minutes later. Carlton just about manages to keep up with a swift striding Sandra whilst following her down the road.

ABOUT THE AUTHOR

David Henningham was born in London in 1970. After living in Leighton Buzzard (Bedfordshire) for three years, he moved to Manchester in 2006. His previous book The Great British Blog Book for Nostalgic Geeks, a collection of raw blogs from his website, retrohen (www.retro-hen.com), was the platform for the Section N Underpass.

David still lives in Manchester.